spirit of the night sky

Laksar Burra

JB BOOKS J.B. BOOKS AUSTRALIA

SPIRIT OF THE NIGHT SKY

This edition published in 2001 by
J.B. Books Pty Ltd,
P. O. Box 118
Marleston South Australia 5033

Ayers Rock Resort

First edition sponsored by Ayres Rock Resort,
Northern Territory Australia in 1988

ISBN 1 876 622 326

Text: Laksar Burra
Illustrations: Luqman McKingley
Cover Design: Latif McKingley
Diagrams: Latif McKingley
Cover Photography: Akira Fuji and Hussein Burra
Photo Credits: Akira Fuji, David Malin and Hussein Burra

Revised edition produced by Phoenix Offset. Printed in Hong Kong

The stars belong to everyone
A Note on Drawing Constellations

When we go from source to source, and book to book, and examine how
astrologers, astronomers and seers have imagined pictures in the stars
~ from place to place and age to age ~ we are struck by several things.
First ~ There are *so* many similarities. Similar ways of connecting stars;
similar images resulting; similar stories and myths. Second ~ Despite
the similarities, nobody seems to agree exactly with anyone else on how
to *draw* the lines or how the images are *positioned*. (If the Greeks had
Virgo right side up, the Romans turned her upside down and had the
virgin holding Libra, the scales of justice.) Third ~ The stars are fun; so
we needn't be too worried about *how* we connect the 'dots' to show *our*
vision. We can even be creative and make up some of our own
constellations. For example, if we take the sting and tail of Scorpius and
join it onto Ara the Altar, we can call it the great Australian racehorse
Phar Lap, whose spirit we can see running through the sky. We can even
make out a jockey riding the horse, with a winner's crown on his head
~ the half circle of stars known as Corona Australis . . . We hope you
approach this little book and drawings with the same spirit of *freedom*.
We hope you'll feel in these pages some of the fun and wonderment
which has inspired every stargazer, young or old, since time began.

Author's Note

I first came to the centre of Australia because I wanted to make some connection with the Aboriginal people and their culture. During my time working here giving guided tours for visitors at Uluru-Kata Tjuta National Park, while continuing my work as a glass-artist, I have come to realise how much the Centre represents the heart and soul of this great continent.

The night skies are truly magnificent out here in the Centre, some of the best that you will find anywhere in the world; and it was my own introduction to these clear night skies that opened up a whole new world to me. As I have learnt more about the planets, stars, and constellations, I have become aware of the wealth of stories which relate to the night sky, and of the many similarities between these stories.

I enjoy telling these to international audiences at 'star-talks' each night at Uluru (Ayers Rock), which has been a story-telling and meeting-place for aboriginal people for many thousands of years, and is now an international meeting-place.

As the essence of my star-talks is embodied in this book, it is my belief and hope that this short guide will convey something of the 'spirit of the night sky' ~ a universal spirit that brings people to feel closer together as One ~ a global family that still appreciates the diversity and uniqueness of different cultures.

Ayers Rock Resort's 'Sounds of Silence' restaurant, where I do my story-telling, provides an excellent venue for people to experience the natural wonders around us, some of which we can no longer appreciate in cities, due to the atmospheric glow of urban illumination.

Laksar Burra
Ayers Rock Resort, 1 October 1998

The brightest stars, the 'Sounds of Silence'

You are invited to have dinner in one of the most magical restaurants anywhere in Australia and possibly the world. Set out in the desert, under the brilliant skies of the Southern Hemisphere, the Sounds of Silence dining experience is one not to be missed.

Instead of walls, this restaurant out in the open air has magnificent views to the distant domes of Kata Tjuta (Olgas), and instead of entertainment there's the stillness of the desert at night, the haunting sound of the breeze through the Desert Oaks, followed by a magical tour of the heavens with an astronomer.

Staged in a clearing in the sand dunes a few kilometres from the Ayers Rock Resort, the evening starts with canapes and a glass of champagne or a cool ale as the sun slowly sets near Kata Tjuta (Olgas), and paints the sky with a vivid palette from burnished orange to intense crimson.

Watching the sky change colour in such an extraordinary fashion is an experience all of its own and one that is often not appreciated, as visitors normally watch the sun's rays fall on the western face of Uluru (Ayers Rock), and don't turn around and watch the sun itself in the western sky. But at the 'Sounds of Silence', you get the best of both sunsets, as you can take in the 360 degree views from the top of a sand dune to: Uluru (Ayers Rock) to the east and Kata Tjuta (Olgas) in the west.

After a gourmet barbecue dinner, the tranquillity of the outback and the spectacular heavens are revealed when the lanterns are extinguished, and conversation is hushed by the sudden darkness. For some people this will be the first time that they ever truly hear the silence of the Australian outback, or in fact true silence anywhere.

Stars which were only partially visible in the light of the bush dining setting are seen in all their brilliance, and you slowly become aware of the utter stillness of the outback at night.

After a few minutes, an astronomer steps out from the dark, taking you on a magical tour of the heavens before inviting you to take a closer look at some of the better known planets through a powerful telescope. Under some of the clearest skies in the world, the astronomer tells the tales of ancient mythologies and the Aboriginal stories of creation and how they are played out in the sky.

Ayers Rock Resort is considered to be one of the best places in the world to star-gaze, because it is free of the pollution and city lights which mask the stars elsewhere. The Sounds of Silence dining experience has become the signature product for Ayers Rock Resort and one that is internationally acclaimed and awarded.

TABLE OF CONTENTS

Introduction

For thousands of years peoples and cultures from all over the world have used planets, stars, constellations and other night-sky phenomena for a multitude of purposes:

To tell the time of year . . . The first rising of Sirius, representing the goddess Isis, marked the beginning of the New Year for the Egyptians.

To find direction . . . The Spanish and the Portuguese used the Southern Cross to navigate in the Southern Hemisphere; the star Canopus is used today in spacecraft navigation.

To know when to find food . . . In South Australia, the appearance of the star Arcturus heralds the time to go looking for the larvae of wood ants.

To teach appropriate behaviour . . . Stories of the Pleiades, seen by the naked eye as a small cluster of six or seven stars, are parables of passion and lust and what may happen if we succumb to these vices.

To explain why things are as they are today . . . Many stories about the creation of the Sun, the Moon, landscape formations and other night-sky phenomena have ancient star-people as Creators.

From time immemorial, the stars have inspired us to reflect on our past, present and on possibilities for the future. If we listen to some of the stories from around the world we may gain valuable insights from the past which may help us to move into the future . . .

Celebrating Creation in the Night Skies

Wherever we go in the world we find people and cultures whose stories celebrate the night skies. The Aboriginal people of South Australia tell the tale of Nurrunderi . . .

Nurrunderi, the Creator, went fishing one day. As it happens, he caught the biggest fish in the Universe.

"Such a magnificent fish requires a special home," the Creator said. So, Nurrunderi created the great Murray River. And Nurrunderi made many other fish and set them in the Murray so the Great Codfish would have friends to play with.

Nurrunderi was tired after all his efforts and needed to rest. His brother-in-law had a quiet place so Nurrunderi decided to stay with him to recuperate.

After a while Nurrunderi felt himself again. But he was lonely. His wives, who usually took care of him, were not there. He missed them very much indeed and decided to find out where his wives had gone while he'd been recuperating.

Until now Nurrunderi had used his magic canoe to travel around the waterways of creation. But Nurrunderi knew his search for his wives would take him far overland and he wouldn't be able to take his canoe with him.

He looked around for a safe place to leave it.

That night, as Nurrunderi was considering his options, he looked up at the night sky and saw a great dark empty space where the canoe would fit perfectly.

Nearby there were two big sand dunes. Nurrunderi stood with one foot on each dune. Then, he dragged his canoe and began to lift it up, higher and higher. The sweat from his exertion ran in rivulets which formed puddles on the ground.

Finally, Nurrunderi succeeded in hoisting his canoe to the safe place in the sky. There, he could keep an eye on it as he travelled in search of his wives.

In South Australia they call it Nurrunderi Juki, the Canoe of Nurrunderi.

We call it the Milky Way . . .

The Milky Way ~ The Creator's Canoe

The Constellation Scorpius the Scorpion

There is a black space in the Milky Way. It is like a dark cloud ~ quite distinct on a clear night with no moon.

It is known as the Coal Sack Nebula.

The Incas saw this black cloud in the Milky Way as a Partridge. Australian Aboriginal people see it as the head of a mighty Emu Bird that flies through the sky.

You can follow this black cloud through the Milky Way and make out his long neck, body, wings and feet.

This great Emu Bird is fully visible in Central Australia flying through the night sky in July and August when the Milky Way is directly overhead.

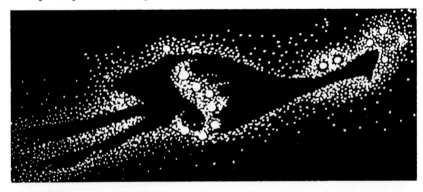

The Pole Star, diagram

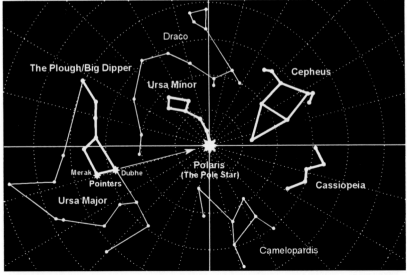

Orientation

One of the first things we need to know when we begin looking at the night skies is how to use the stars to orientate ourselves.

The simplest way to orientate ourselves with the sky is to start by finding a point of the compass (N, E, S, or W). The crudest but simplest way of doing this is to look where the sun set, because this is West. Directly opposite West is East; and from this it is quite easy to find North and South.

After dark in the Northern Hemisphere people can use the Pole Star, Polaris, to locate themselves, simply by locating Polaris ~ the star whose direction is *North*.

When the Celts and Druids travelled, they told stories that featured the landscape in much that same way that the Aboriginal people here do today. They probably used Polaris and its surrounding stars to orientate themselves.

However, Polaris would not be much use to them in Australia as it cannot be seen in the Southern Hemisphere because it is, literally, 'under the ground'.

In the Southern Hemisphere we do not have a pole star, so we need to be a little bit more creative to find due South.

Three methods are available, with varying degrees of accuracy. We learn three methods of finding South because, depending on where you are, one or another of these guiding star groups may not be visible. The problem for those navigating by the stars is that sometimes we can not see any of them at all.

First Method: The Southern Cross

The Southern Cross, known to astronomers as **Crux**, affords us the first method ~ the most accurate way of finding South, together with the two pointers **Alpha** and **Beta Centauri**.

There are five main stars in Crux ~ the stars we find on the Australian flag. There is a sixth star on the Australian flag which represents Federation. On Australia Day 26th, January 1901 Australia became a Nation. The six -sided star is found on the flag but not in the sky.

To find South you draw an imaginary line from Gamma Crux through to Alpha Crux, and follow this line through the sky. Of course, you have to know when to stop. You join the two pointer stars with a line, divide this line in half, then at right angles draw another imaginary line through the sky until it meets the line from the Southern Cross. This point is the South Celestial Pole. If you drop a line from this point to the horizon you will be facing South.

Finding South using the Southern Cross.

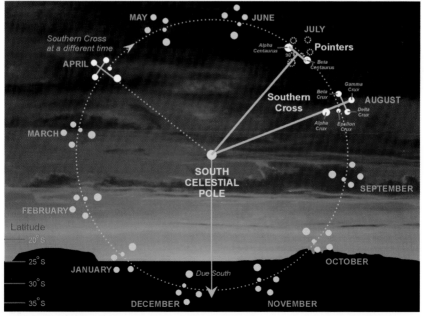

The Southern Cross

The Portugese naturalist Cristoval d'Costa referred to the Southern Cross and the two pointers as the South Celestial Clock.

In Aboriginal mythology, there are several stories that relate to the Southern Cross.

One story, from a coastal region, describes the two pointers as the fins of a shark chasing a stingray, the Cross, around the sky. Another, from Central Australia, describes the Cross as the footprint of the wedge-tailed eagle. The black area, the Coal Sack, next to the Cross is his nest and the two pointers are his throwing sticks.

The two pointers are often connected with the origin of fire. One of the many stories about how fire spread throughout Australia comes from the northwest coast . . .

The Smokey Way

Two brothers, Kanbi and Jittibidi, were sitting around a campfire high up in the sky, in the area of the Southern Cross, with their two firesticks resting beside them. Food was running out up there so the brothers came down to Earth to hunt, bringing their firesticks to light their way.

They set up camp and then went off in search of the brush-tail possum. They did not need their firesticks because the moon was up, so they left them at the camp.

The brothers were gone for a long time. The two firesticks back at camp began to get bored and decided to play a game of hide and seek. They played among the dead logs and dry spinifex grass . . . Soon a huge bushfire started.

The two brothers saw its smoke rising on the horizon. They knew what had happened, so they returned to camp at once, picked up their firesticks and flew back to the sky ~ so that no further damage would be done.

The smoke rising from those fire sticks can still be seen, floating through the sky as the Milky Way.

A group of Aboriginal people out hunting saw the firesticks ~ and, for the first time, fire, They felt its warmth, realised its benefit and took home a burning log and stored this firebrand in the Mulga tree. Mulga is still the Aboriginal people's preferred wood for fires and fire-lighting throughout much of Australia.

Second Method: Canopus and Achernar

The second method of orientating ourselves to true South, uses two stars: Canopus (the second brightest star in sky) and Achernar.

Make a large equilateral triangle using these stars. The third imaginary point will be the South Celestial Pole. Drop a line to the horizon for due South.

Achernar is the brightest star in the constellation Eridanus the River.

Canopus is the brightest star in the constellation of Carina the Keel. This is the keel of the ship jason and the Argonauts used when they went in search of the golden fleece.

In Japan and China, Canopus is very difficult to see ~ so if you do catch a glimpse of it low on the horizon you are considered fortunate as you will be blessed with peace, happiness and a long life . . .

Finding South using Canopus and Achernar

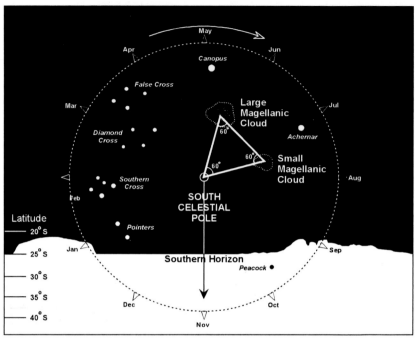

How to find South using the Magellanic Clouds

Third Method: The Magellanic Clouds
The third method of finding South uses two faint clouds in the southern sky.

These are the Large and Small Magellanic Clouds. These two clouds are the closest satellite galaxies to our own. The Large Magellanic Cloud contains about 10,000 million stars and lies about 170,000 light years away. The Small Magellanic Cloud has about 2,000 million stars and is a bit further away, about 190,000 light years.

The Magellanic Clouds may not be seen clearly, if at all, when the Moon is in the sky. To find South using these clouds we make an equilateral triangle, the third point of which is the South Celestial Pole. We just need to drop a line to the horizon to find South.

Large Magellanic Cloud

Small Magellanic Cloud

The Magellanic Clouds appear in several Aboriginal stories. One story describes the clouds as the camps of an old man and woman, the Jukara, who are no longer able to hunt their own food.

Food is brought to them by the star people, who bring them fish and lily bulbs from the great river in the sky, the Milky Way.

The old man is represented by the Large Magellanic Cloud, and the old woman is represented by the Small Magellanic Cloud. The space between them is where their fires are, and the bright star Achernar, in the constellation Eridanus the River, represents their meal. This is probably a story to remind people to respect their elders.

What is the South Celestial Pole?

The North and South Poles are the pivots around which the Earth rotates, and around which the stars *appear* to be turning. The South Pole is the southernmost point of the Earth's rotational axis.

The South Celestial Pole is simply an extension of the Earth's rotational axis into the sky. The North Celestial Pole is also an extension into the sky, which happens to pass almost directly through the bright star, **Polaris** ~ seen from the Northern Hemisphere.

If we could stand on the Equator, the South Celestial Pole would be seen on the horizon as we look south, and Polaris would be seen, if we look north.

As we move away from the Equator, say to the south, the South Celestial Pole rises higher in the sky and Polaris disappears beneath the horizon.

We can calculate latitude by measuring the angle of the South Celestial Pole from the horizon.

Star trails around the South Celestial Pole

Constellations: Maps in the Sky

On a good night we can see about two or three thousand stars of the zillions that are out there. Most of the stars we see have been named.

Throughout history, human eyes have pulled certain stars together and drawn shapes with these groups of stars reflecting the knowledge and beliefs of the time. As the star lore of societies advanced, the people mapped these shapes in the stars in the same way that Australia or any other country is mapped on the ground. These mapped shapes became the constellations we know today.

If we were to turn the map of Australia around in our hands it would look different, but it is still the same map of Australia. This is how it is with the night skies. As the earth moves, our view of the sky 'map' changes.

Our view of the sky 'map' is also changed by our own movement. When we travel about the Earth, we change our view of objects in the sky. For example, the crescent of the waxing moon in the Northern Hemisphere looks like the waning moon in the Southern Hemisphere; and many constellations appear upside down in the Southern Hemisphere because they were mapped by people who viewed them from the Northern Hemisphere.

Take, for example, the constellation, Leo The Lion, an autumn-winter constellation visible from February to July in the *Southern* Hemisphere. The lion's head and mane are identified by a sickle of stars or 'question mark'. The lion appears to be upside down and crouching. In the *Northern* Hemisphere, the lion is right side up.

There are 88 officially recognised constellations that were adopted by the International Astronomical Union in 1930. Thirteen of these are the constellations our sun passes across as it makes its way through the heavens each year; and, of these, twelve are also known as the astrological birth signs or 'The Signs of the Zodiac'.

The Constellation Leo, the Lion

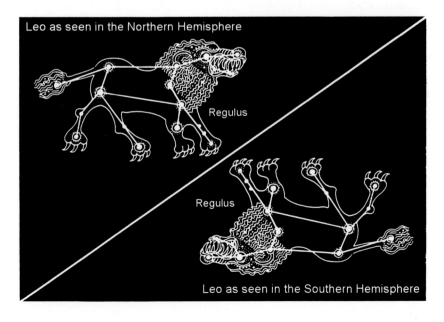

Leo as seen in the Northern Hemisphere

Regulus

Regulus

Leo as seen in the Southern Hemisphere

CANCER
CANCER

Castor

GEMINI
GEMINI

Pollux

Gateway
of Souls

The Milky Way

Betelgeuse

ORION
ORION

Great
Orion
Nebula
(M42)

Saiph

NOTE: In order to show the Constellations plainly, we look at them as they appear in the Northern Sky. Turn these pages upside down to see them in their Southern Sky positions.

As the Earth moves, the Signs of the Zodiac appear to track from East to West through the sky.

When one sign disappears below the Western horizon a new constellation will be appearing on the Eastern horizon.

They cannot all be seen at the same time, because some will quite literally be 'below' the ground.

When you look for the Signs of the Zodiac, stand facing North, then look over your left shoulder towards the West where one of the signs will be setting and then follow back around to North and then East where another sign will be rising. If you face South they will be more difficult to find.

The Earth is moving in two ways:

It is *spinning* on its own axis, causing day and night. Consequently, the stars will appear to move across the sky throughout the night. The stars will continue to do this during the day, but the sun is too bright for us to see them.

The Earth is also *orbiting* the Sun, creating the seasons of the year ~ as the Earth has a 23.5 degree axial tilt which causes the Sun to favour either the Northern or Southern Hemisphere.

This movement of the Earth around the Sun also causes the constellations to appear in different parts of the sky at different times of year.

Thus people are born under different constellations which we know as the Signs of the Zodiac. At any time, six of the signs will be visible on clear nights. They follow each other in the order :

Aries, Taurus, Gemini, Cancer, Leo, Virgo, Libra, Scorpius, Sagittarius, Capricorn, Aquarius, Pisces.

Reference is usually made to these twelve signs only; the thirteenth constellation our sun passes through is Ophiuchus, the serpent holder, an old constellation representing a man encircled by a snake.

Ophiuchus appears after Scorpius.

Near the Zodiac Signs in the sky, are other constellations equally or more famous.

In this book, the constellations are depicted as you would see them in the Northern Hemisphere, so the images are immediately understandable. To see how they appear in our Southern Hemisphere, just turn the Constellation Map pages upside down.

Aries The Ram

The Arabs knew Aries as a Sheep, the Chinese saw it as a Dog. We Westerners know Aries as a Ram because it is said to represent The Golden Fleece sought by Jason and the Argonauts.

This Greek myth tells of a flying golden Ram which was looked after by Aries, the god of war. Hermes, messenger to the gods, sent the Ram to save some children who had a wicked stepmother. One of the children died during the escape, whilst the other flew away on the Ram. The boy was so pleased to have escaped, that he sacrificed the Ram to give thanks to the gods. He gave the fleece to King Aeetes. The Golden Fleece had magical powers and was guarded by a dragon that never slept.

Jason, a Prince of Thessaly, was famous for his brave adventures. He was determined to reclaim his throne, which had been wrongfully taken by his uncle, Pelias, who had murdered Jason's father, King Aeson. Pelias promised he would give the throne back to Jason only if he could bring him the Golden Fleece. This was an impossible task. But Jason immediately set sail on 'The Argo', with his crew of Argonauts. He found the Golden Fleece guarded by King Aeetes' dragon.

The King promised it to Jason if he succeeded in passing some difficult tests. Jason passed all tests, but King Aeetes went back on his word. The King's daughter, Medea, however, fell in love with Jason and put a spell on the dragon, so Jason was able to get the Golden Fleece and return home with it, and, with Medea, whom he married.

Taurus the Bull

Taurus the Bull can be seen in the evening sky from October to March and it is quite easily identified.

The red star **Aldebaran** is the bull's eye in the 'v' shape of stars know as Hyades. It has long horns tipped by 2 stars and its feet go off to the other side. A cluster of stars known as the Pleiades make up its tail.

Most countries around the world have a story relating to the **Pleiades** or **Seven Sisters**.

The Seven Sisters story is part of an Aboriginal Songline that goes from the East Coast to the West Coast of Australia. In Central Australia they say that seven beautiful women were seen by the hunter, Wati Nehru. He desired them all, but particularly the youngest because she was the prettiest. The women said Wati Nehru was ugly and had big feet. They tried to stay well clear of him. But he kept trying to catch them. The chase goes on, it is said, even today.

Gemini the Twins

The two main stars in this constellation are **Castor** and **Pollux**.

In the Greek legend, Castor and Pollux were the sons of Queen Leda of Sparta but they had different fathers. Castor's father was the King of Sparta while Pollux's father was the god Zeus.

In Roman mythology Castor and Pollux were seen as Romulus and Remus, the founders of Rome.

You will see that Pollux is slightly brighter than Castor. Castor was born of mortal stock whereas Pollux was of heavenly parentage and therefore brighter.

One day Castor died and Pollux was so upset over his brother's death, that he begged his father not to be separated from Castor. There was not much Zeus could do other than place them side by side in the sky.

These two stars represent the heads of the twins whom you can see apparently standing upside down with their feet in the great river of the Milky Way.

These two stars, Castor and Pollux, are also know as the patron saints of mariners.

Cancer the Crab

This is the faintest of the Zodiac constellations in the night sky. You will not be able to see it when the moon is up.

There is a cluster of stars in its centre known as the Beehive Cluster. Ancient Greek philosophers described it as the Gateway souls pass through on leaving heaven before entering the world.

In Christian mythology the cluster is described as the manger of the baby Jesus and the stars on either side as the ox and the ass.

The Greeks tell the story how Hercules was out fighting Hydra, a horrible sea monster with several heads. It was an incredible battle witnessed by the Crab, who took sides with Hydra and attacked Hercules by biting him on the foot. Hercules retaliated by stepping on him and crushing him under his mighty foot. Later on, the Crab was raised high, up into the night sky.

Orion the Hunter, is *not* a Zodiac constellation, but appears 'at the feet of' the Twins, Gemini, and is easily recognised in both Northern and Southern Hemispheres. It appears upside down in the Southern skies where it is seen in summer.

In Greek mythology it is said that Orion the Hunter was an arrogant chap who was stung to death by a scorpion. The constellation of Orion stands in the sky opposite the constellation of Scorpius.

In the Southern Hemisphere, the appearance of Orion marks the beginning of the summer, while the appearance of Scorpio marks the beginning of winter.

Orion and Canis Major

The star **Betelgeuse**, a red supergiant, between 300-400 times the size of our own sun, represents Orion's right shoulder; **Bellatrix**, his left shoulder.

Rigel is a blue-white star representing Orion's left leg and **Saiph**, his right leg. In the middle, is Orion's Belt of three stars, his Sword hanging from the belt. In the middle of Orion's Sword is **M42** or the Great Orion Nebula, a star-birth region of the sky.

Orion is seen as above in the Northern Hemisphere

Orion is seen upside down in the Southern Hemisphere

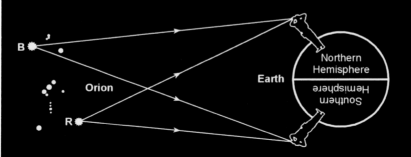

A person in the Northern Hemisphere sees the star Betelgeuse (**B**) 'above' the star Rigel (**R**) Turn the book upside down to show that a viewer in the Southern Hemisphere will see Rigel above Betelgeuse -- the whole constellation of Orion The Hunter appears upside down, with the three stars of the Hunter's Belt appearing below his 'sword'

Orion has two hunting dogs: **Canis Major**, the 'Big Dog', and **Canis Minor**, the 'Lesser Dog'. 'Big Dog' is easily recognisable by the star **Sirius**, also known as the Dog Star, the brightest star in the sky. It is easy to draw a 'stick-dog' with this constellation, by 'connecting the dots' of its stars.

The three bright stars of Orion's belt and the three fainter stars of his sword are quickly identifiable. On a clear night with no moon, Orion's shield and baton are also visible as he brandishes them at Taurus the Bull.

In Australia, Orion's Belt and sword are commonly known as 'The Saucepan'. In Melbourne, Australia, it is sometimes called 'The Melbourne Shopping Trolley'.

The Blackfoot Indians of North America saw Orion's Belt as the Arrowhead of a mighty warrior. In Alaska, the Inuit saw the three stars of the sword as three steps cut into a bank of snow, leading to three kayaks by the water's edge, being the three stars of the Belt.

Osiris, Keeper of the Dead

The Ancient Egyptians saw Orion as Osiris who ruled the heavenly Kingdom of the Dead . . .

The sky goddess Nut had several children. Osiris was her eldest son. He was the god who became Egypt's first ruler. His reign was a dynamic and prosperous time when Osiris showed people how to bring order into their lives.

The Egyptians call Sirius, Isis, sister and consort of Osiris. The appearance of Sirius marked the beginning of their New Year and the time of the flooding of the Nile.

Osiris' brother, Seth, was envious of Osiris' role and power and conspired to murder him. Seth cut Osiris' body into thousands of pieces and scattered them throughout Egypt.

Osiris' lover ~ his sister Isis ~ was devastated by his death. They had no children, leaving Osiris without an heir. Isis used her powers to find all of Osiris' body parts and put them back together.

In this way, she was able to make love with Osiris once more; to receive his seed and became pregnant.

Osiris returned to the heavens. He became Orion, the Keeper of the Kingdom of Duat, the Dead.

Meanwhile, Isis had a son, Horus, who grew up and challenged his uncle, Seth, for the right to rule Egypt. A fight ensued in which Horus lost an eye and Seth lost his testicles. The Sun God intervened, ended the conflict and made Horus ruler of Egypt.

Sirius is a binary star. It appears as a single star to the naked eye, but large telescopes show two stars. There is a small white dwarf star, sometimes referred to as 'The Pup', or 'Sirius B', that orbits the larger star every 50 years.

Sirius B consists of matter so dense that just one teaspoon of it would weigh about a ton.

Western astronomers only discovered this little white dwarf about 135 years ago. It is invisible even with most modern telescopes. Yet, an African people ~ the Dogon from Mali ~ have known many facts about this binary system for thousands of years, and this is part of their secret and sacred ceremonies.

The Dogon say our human civilisation actually originated from Sirius and that the Nomos, or the 'Fish Gods', came from this star system. Ancient Babylonian and Egyptian murals depict such Fish Gods.

The Dogon also say that there is a third star, Sirius C, which is accompanied by a satellite they call 'Star of Women' which they symbolise by a cross. Astronomers are looking for evidence of this third star now.

How did the Dogon obtain their knowledge of this complex star system? They believe it was brought to them by the Nomos; but it remains a mystery to us.

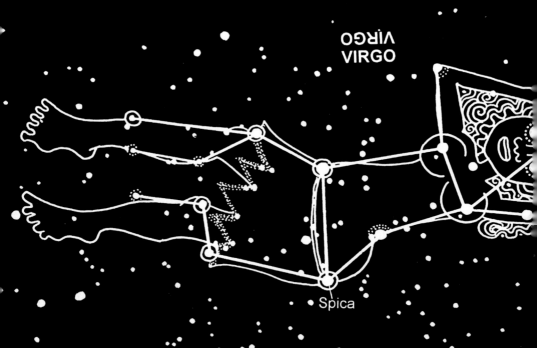

VIRGO

Spica

NOTE: In order to show the Constellations plainly, we look at them as they appear in the Northern Sky. Turn these pages upside down to see them in their Southern Sky positions.

Coma
Berenicies

LEO
LEO

Leo the Lion

The sphinx in Egypt probably relates to the constellation, Leo. The Egyptians saw Leo as the emblem representing fire and heat. In modern astrology it is the house of the sun that rules the heart.

In Greek mythology, Hercules was said to have killed the Lion as the first of his twelve labours. In the Middle Ages Christians saw Leo as one of Daniel's lions. There are many stories relating to Leo the Lion. There is a famous one in Shakespeare's 'A Midsummer Night's Dream', *the tragic story of* **Pyramus and Thisbe . . .**

Two young lovers, Pyramus and Thisbe, had parents who refused to let them marry, so they could only talk to each other through a gap in the wall between their houses.

One day they arranged to meet outside the city limits, under a mulberry tree that was laden with white berries.

The day for their meeting came.

While Thisbe was waiting for her love to arrive, a lioness, with jaws bloody from a kill, appeared before her.

Terrified, poor Thisbe ran to hide, dropping her veil behind her. The lioness snatched the veil in its jaws, tearing it and smothering it with blood.

When Pyramus came across the lion's tracks, they led him to Thisbe's blood-stained veil. Thinking his lover was dead, he fell upon his own sword in anguish.

Soon after, Thisbe returned, saw her lover lying dead and took her own life as well, by falling on Pyramus' sword.

The blood of the two lovers mingled together in the earth. It rose up through the roots and the trunk of the mulberry tree until it reached the fruit. Mulberries have been red ever since.

At the tail end of the constellation Leo, there is a delicate triangular constellation known as **Coma Berenices**, said to represent Thisbe's veil. The God Zeus put it there to warn parents that they must never, ever deny young love.

Virgo the Virgin

In Greek mythology, this constellation is the Goddess Demeter, holding in her hand an ear of wheat, represented by the star **Spica**.

In Roman mythology she is Astra, Goddess of Justice. The scales of justice themselves are represented by the constellation Libra.

The Greeks tell the story of Demeter, Goddess of Fertility, who had a young daughter called Persephone. She was young and beautiful and loved by all.

One day Persephone was out dancing amongst the spring blossoms when she was seen by Hades, Lord of the Underworld. Quite naturally he fell in love with her, and on one of his rare trips to the Upper World, he abducted her and took her back to his Kingdom and made her his Queen.

The Goddess Demeter, missing her young daughter, roamed the earth for several days in search of her.

She couldn't find her any where. In anger and grief she called out to the gods that if her daughter were not returned she would withdraw her powers of fertility and the Earth would become barren.

Zeus intervened and spoke with Hades, and they agreed that Persephone would be returned to Demeter, providing she had eaten none of the food of the Underworld. However Persephone had already eaten a few pomegranate seeds, so it looked as though her fate was sealed and she would spend the rest of her life with Hades.

Demeter was grief stricken. Zeus, feeling sorry for her, declared that Persephone must spend six months with Hades, creating Autumn and Winter on Earth, and six months with her mother Demeter, giving Earth Spring and Summer.

This is also the reason, it is said, why we only see this constellation for six months of the year.

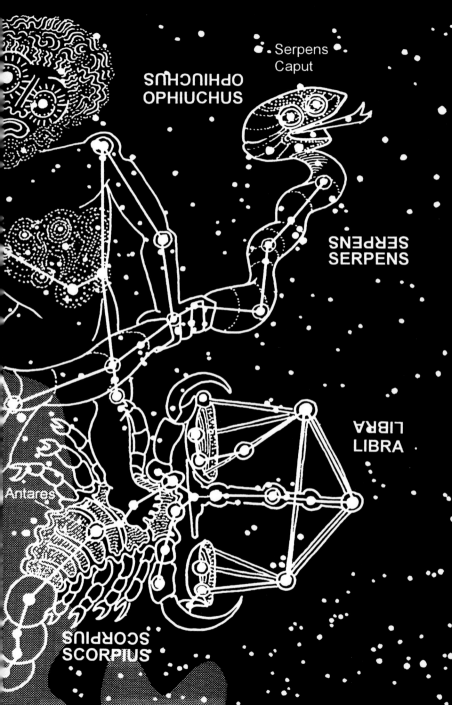

Serpens
Caput

OHIUCHUS (upside down)
OPHIUCHUS

SERPENS (upside down)
SERPENS

LIBRA (upside down)
LIBRA

Antares

SCORPIUS (upside down)
SCORPIUS

NOTE: In order to show the Constellations plainly, we look at them as they appear in the Northern Sky. Turn these pages upside down to see them in their Southern Sky positions.

Libra the Scales

Libra is the only one of the classical Zodiac constellations which does not depict a human or an animal form.

At one time Libra did represent the claws of the giant scorpion, Scorpius. Later, under the directive of Julius Caesar, the Romans decided to separate it and make an independent constellation with its own group of stars forming the scales of justice. Perhaps Caesar saw himself holding the balance.

It is possible that Libra was drawn out when it was on the Equinox and was seen to represent a balance of equal day and night.

In China it was known as the Star of Longevity which they called Sho-Sing.

Scorpius the Scorpion

Scorpius is a large, easily recognisable constellation in the winter night sky. It was once part of a larger constellation which included Libra, the Scales.

Scorpius was said to have been sent by Gaia to kill Orion by stinging him on his heel because he had boasted that he could kill all the wild beasts of the land. This is why, when Scorpius appears on the eastern horizon, the constellation Orion will be disappearing on the western horizon.

In the Southern Hemisphere the appearance of Scorpius marks the beginning of winter. There is a large red star in Scorpius, **Antares**, rival to Mars, and about 300 times the size of our Sun.

When the Aboriginal people from Yirrkala in the North saw Scorpius in the early morning sky, they expected then to see Indonesian traders in the Gulf of Carpentaria.

The Maori people see Scorpius as the fish hook used by their legendary hero, Maui. They say Maui went fishing with his brothers because their people were hungry. But when the sea became choppy, his brothers were frightened to go out of sight of land and they returned.

Maui was determined to catch something so he threw his line and hook into the sea. He waited a while, then he felt a tug and he began to haul in the line. He thought he must have caught a whopper because he had to pull and strain so hard. Indeed it was no ordinary catch. He had pulled up a land mass from the bottom of the sea. The land splintered, fractured in two and became the North and South Islands of New Zealand. The force was so great that the fishhook sprang back into the sky where it has been seen ever since.

Ophiuchus the Serpent Holder

It is generally understood that there are twelve signs to the Zodiac. However, some claim that Ophiuchus is the thirteenth sign. It lies roughly between Scorpius and Sagittarius. A thirteenth star sign is problematic for the Zodiac and is usually omitted.

Ophiuchus is encoiled by a serpent, known as the constellation Serpens which has two parts, Serpens Caput, the Serpent's Head, and Serpens Cauda, the Serpents Tail. Ophiuchus' left foot holds the scorpion down.

Ophiuchus is usually referred to as the healer Aesculapius, son of Apollo. It is said that Apollo and the centaur Chiron trained Ophiuchus in the arts of medicine, and that he had the power of awakening the dead.

For many years, the Caduceus, a winged staff entwined with snakes ~ derived from Ophiuchus ~ has been the symbol for the medical profession.

Sagittarius the Archer

Associated with Chiron the centaur, Sagittarius the Archer is sitting on a horse and with his bow he is said to be aiming an arrow at the heart of Scorpius, killing him.

Scorpius had previously killed Orion for his boastful ways, under the instructions of Artemis, the Goddess of Hunting, so this is a story of payback, or an eye for an eye and a tooth for a tooth!

Sagittarius is also known as "The Teapot" and, when drawn out in the sky, may be more easily recognised as a teapot than as a centaur. On a clear night with no moon, the Milky Way is said to represent the steam coming out of the teapot.

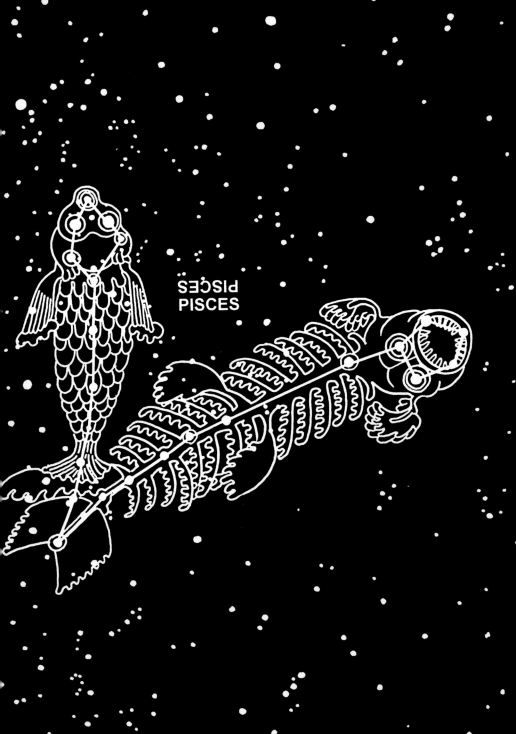

PISCES

NOTE: In order to show the Constellations plainly, we look at them as they appear in the Northern Sky. Turn these pages upside down to see them in their Southern Sky positions.

AQUARIUS
QUARIUS

CAPRICORN
CAPRICORN

Corona Australis is a constellation which can be seen in the Southern Hemisphere in the winter sky and it is also known as the Southern Crown. It lies next to Sagittarius the Archer and is said to be *his* crown.

In Greek Mythology, this constellation was known as the Wheel of Fire.

Zeus, king of the gods ~ or Jupiter in Roman mythology ~ was married to the beautiful goddess Hera.

They had a tempestuous relationship, perhaps because she was also his sister. Zeus and Hera had an argument and Hera left in a rage to be by herself for a while.

While she was away Hera was seen by Ixion, who had always desired her. Seizing the perfect opportunity, Ixion attempted to seduce Hera, but she fooled him by putting a cloud, which assumed her shape, into her bed. While he was drunk, Ixion mated with the cloud instead of Hera.

When Zeus found out *he* flew into an uncontrollable rage. He made an enormous wheel of fire and went in search of Ixion. When he found him, Zeus lashed Ixion to this wheel of fire and flung him into the sky.

Poor Ixion still rolls through the heavens suffering this eternal punishment ~ as a warning to us all.

Capricorn the Fish Goat

Capricorn is drawn as a goat with a fish's tail.

Fish gods belong to very ancient mythologies so Capricorn probably dates back to very earliest times.

In Greek mythology, Capricorn is the goat-god, Pan, who got his fish's tail when he jumped into a river to escape from the monster, Typhon.

This constellation has also been known as the Gate of the Gods because Platonists considered it to be the gateway souls had to pass through when they left this earthly life on their journey back to the heavens.

Capricorn can also be drawn as a church with a steeple, and may be more easily recognised as such than as a fish-goat.

Capricorn has also been known as the Mansion of Kings since Roman times. It was Julius Caesar's birth sign.

Aquarius The Water Carrier

This constellation shows the figure of a man or a boy pouring water or wine from a cup, jar or urn.

In almost all ancient mythologies ~ Arabian, Chinese, Egyptian, Euphratian, Babylonian, Greek, Roman ~ Aquarius is associated with water: sometimes as the life-giving rain; sometimes as the sea; and sometimes, with inundation, deluge, flood and storm.

Aquarius is not conspicuous and we need to look carefully for the 'Y' shape (four stars) of the cup or water vessel.

Pisces The Fishes

Pisces, the final Zodiac constellation, is drawn as two fishes joined together by their tails.

Ancient legends vary in their explanations of Pisces, sometimes seen as one fish, sometimes as two ~ representing duality. In early astrology Pisces was thought to be under the influence of the sea god Neptune.

In Roman times, the two fishes were said to have earned their place in the sky because they carried Venus and her son Cupid to safety when they were being chased by the monster Typhon.

The fish is a symbol of the early Christian faith and it has been suggested that the fish in Pisces symbolise those used by Christ in the miraculous 'feeding of the multitudes'.

Corona Borealis is the counterpart to Corona Australis. It is seen in the northern part of the sky on winter evenings in the Southern Hemisphere.

In Greek mythology, Ariadne wore a beautiful jewelled crown when she married Bacchus, and he is said to have tossed it up into the sky to mark the happy event.

The Celts of the Ancient Isle of Britain saw Corona Borealis as Caer Arianrhod, more commonly known as the Castle of the Silver Wheel.

Many Australian Aboriginal people see this constellation as a boomerang flying through the sky. The Shawnee Indians of North America see this half circle of stars as dancing maidens.

The White Hawk Feathers

A silver basket came down from the sky to the Earth. Out of the basket emerged seven beautiful maidens. These girls were sisters who began to dance in a circle. Algon, the Shawnee White Hawk Hunter, was passing by when he saw them. From afar, Algon watched these beautiful maidens dancing on the prairie grass. After a while, he fell in love with the youngest. Algon changed himself into a field mouse and crept into the circle of dancing maidens. That night, he changed back to human form and took the younger sister in his arms. The other sisters leapt into their silver basket and fled back into the night sky. The sister who remained began to struggle in Algon's arms; but soon she realised that, far from hurting her, he was kind and gentle. So she agreed to stay with him. They were married. They had a young son. In time, the girl made herself another silver basket.

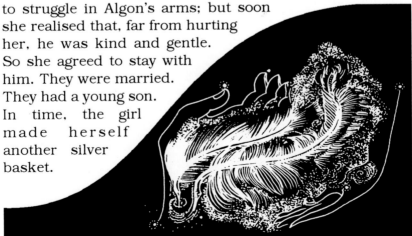

One day, while Algon was hunting, she returned to the night sky with her young son in her basket. When Algon came home, he realised where they had gone. He followed them and gave each a White Hawk's feather. "With this feather," he said, "you can travel on Earth *and* in the Sky!" The sisters still return to dance today; they are the stars in the half-circle of the Corona Borealis.

Arcturus, an old, giant orange star in the constellation called *Bootes the Herdsman*, or the *Bear Keeper*, was said to be the keeper of the *Big* and *Little Bears*, commonly known as the *Big Dipper* and the *Little Dipper* in the Northern Hemisphere.

The Herdsman was named Icarius. He was killed by villains, who dumped his body under a tree. Icarius' body was discovered by his good friend, Dionysus, the God of Wine. With great sadness, love and respect for his dead friend, Dionysus immortalised him by placing him in the sky.

Arcturus was also important to the Aboriginal people as this story from South Australia shows:

The Wise Old Woman Star

Many thousands of years ago there was a wise old woman called Marpeankurruic who was out searching for food in the bush. Her people were starving, during a long period of drought. She searched and searched. She overturned logs and dug into holes with her digging stick but found neither lizard nor snake nor even any grass seeds or fruit. She sat down in despair. Then she saw a small movement: a tiny wood ant going down into a nest. The old woman grabbed her stick and started digging frantically and when she opened the ant's nest, she found it full of wood-ant larvae. She tried one and found it delicious. She fed on the larvae and then gathered up as many as she could and hurried back to her camp. These larvae of the wood-ant saved her whole people from starvation, so when Marpeankurruic died, she went up into the sky and became a star. That's how Aboriginal people know it is time to go looking for larvae of wood-ants: when Arcturus, the wise old woman star, appears in the night sky.

Hydra the Water Snake,
Corvus the Crow and Crater the Cup.

The constellation which contains these characters can be seen above Cancer the Crab and Leo the Lion.

Corvus the Crow belonged to Apollo, God of the Sun . . .

One day, Apollo was very thirsty, so he sent Corvus, his crow, with a cup to collect some water. When Corvus approached the nearest waterhole, he saw a fig tree and, glutton that he was, he stopped for a feed. Soon he realised he was terribly late, so he rushed to the waterhole.

When he got there, he saw Hydra the water-snake. Corvus suddenly had a brilliant idea. He attacked and killed this snake and brought it back to Apollo.

Lying through his beak, the crow told Apollo that the snake had caused him to be late. Being a god, Apollo knew that Corvus was lying; and, anyway, he could clearly see the evidence ~ a sticky mess of fig seeds on Corvus' beak. So Apollo banished the Crow, Cup and Snake, all three, to be fixed in the sky as a reminder to everyone to be punctual and honest at all times.

Vega, the 5th brightest star in the sky, is in the constellation of Lyra. At the moment the Pole Star is Polaris. However, 12-13,000 years from now Vega will be the Pole Star because of the effects of precession ~ the wobble of the Earth as it spins.

In the Southern Hemisphere, Vega can be seen in the northern part of the sky from July to December. It is low on the horizon to the left of the Milky Way. To its right is another bright star, Deneb, in Cygnus the Swan, which is said to show a swan flying down the Milky Way.

Cygnus the Swan is a constellation which is also referred to as the Northern Cross because it has a distinctive cross shape but it is much bigger than the Southern Cross. Cygnus symbolises a swan gliding through the Milky Way.

In Greek mythology, Zeus disguised himself as a swan, to visit Leda, another man's wife. They had a son, Pollux, one of the twins in the constellation Gemini . . .

There are many interesting objects found in Cygnus, but of particular note is **Beta Cygnus**, which is one of the most beautiful double stars. It consists of a yellow giant and its companion, a blue star.

To the right of Cygnus is **Altair**, a bright star in Aquila the Eagle ~ a great bird said to have carried Zeus' thunderbolts.

48

Vega, Altair and **Deneb** together form the Winter Triangle. In the Northern Hemisphere it is known as the Summer Triangle.

The constellations of **Lyra and Aquila** have a story told about them throughout China, Korea and Japan. In this story Vega and Altair, the brightest stars of Lyra and Aquila, are the two main characters:

Vega, a weaver-girl, is the daughter of the Sun God. Altair is a handsome cattle-boy who herds his cattle by the great river in the sky, the Milky Way.

Vega was very lonely so her father decided to find her a husband to make her days more enjoyable. The Sun God saw the cattle-boy and decided that he was the perfect match for his daughter.

It was not long before they were married. However, the young couple spent far too much time indulging in marital pleasures. The cattle were not being fed or watered and began to starve.

When the Sun God saw what was happening, he decided something had to be done, and separated the young couple. Vega was to stay on one side of the river and Altair on the other.

However, to ensure that their marital duties would not be entirely neglected, the Sun God struck a deal with the magpie-geese. On the seventh day of the seventh month every year, thousands of magpie-geese would fly down to the river and form a bridge. Vega would then make the journey across them to see her husband on the other side.

There was one flaw in this arrangement: it is subject to the twists and turns of fate. For, if it happens to rain on this appointed day, the magpie-geese have to take shelter, and the bridge cannot be formed.

The unlucky couple must wait for another year to meet.

Incidentally, this story also explains why magpie geese are bald: Vega walks across their heads every year.

Sun, Planets, Moons

Wiriupranili, The Sun Woman

A story from the centre of Australia describes how the Creator, Mudunkula, gives her daughter, Wiriupranili the Sun, the task of bringing light so that people and animals can see their way around during the day.

Very early each morning, Wiriupranili lights a small fire, the first light, when animals awake and sing their prayers to the One Creator.

Wiriupranili makes herself beautiful by throwing red ochre dust over herself. This is why we have amazing red sunrises in Central Australia. Wiriupranili then lights a huge firestick and begins her journey across the sky, bringing light to people and animals.

In the middle of the day, she rests a while and has something to eat before continuing her journey to the West. There she sets up camp, lights a small fire, puts out her great firestick, and, while resting beside a celestial pool, she dusts herself with red ochre dust again. This is why we have glorious red sunsets in the Centre.

Now, Wiriupranili makes her journey back to the East, but this time her journey takes her through an underground cavern. On her way she prepares for the day's work ahead. When she reaches the East, she starts all over again.

There are many meanings given to the planets. They were used by the Greeks, and other ancients, as a basis for astrology. Astrology ~ the esoteric study of the influences of the heavenly bodies on an individual's life ~ remains very much alive today.

The planets were considered by the Greeks to be gods. Today, we use the Roman names for the planets. For instance, Jupiter is the Roman name for the Greek god Zeus.

Each planet, or god, ruled different aspects of life, parts of the human body, and forces of nature.

Barnumbir, The Morning Star

In Arnhem Land, the Aboriginal people call Planet Venus, 'The Morning Star', Barnumbir. Her appearance at dawn was very important to all women in their preparation for the daily hunting and gathering.

Barnumbir, it is told, was afraid of drowning, so two women attached a long string to her each day before they released her into the sky. The string prevented her from rising too high and drowning in the river of the Milky Way. At daybreak each morning, the women would pull her back and put her in a basket where she would stay during the day.

The Solar System

We are moving, Not the stars. The stars do in fact move, but so *slowly* that it would take thousands of years for us to notice.
So where is our planet ?
It lies within a solar system within a galaxy within the Universe ~ some say within other universes as well.
The Solar System is the name we give to the part of our universe that contains our Sun and the planets that revolve around it. Planet Earth is one of nine planets revolving around the Sun.

The Sun is, in fact, a star, a ball of burning gas.
It is hundreds of times larger than the planets. Our Sun is just one, and not even a particularly large one, of about 100,000 million stars in our galaxy, The Milky Way.

From the Greek word *planetes*, meaning 'wanderers', the **Planets** look like stars in our skies but they move differently and are made of different substances ~ a combination of rock and gases.
Unlike stars, planets are not burning. The reason we see them is the same reason we see the Moon: they *reflect* sunlight.
Stars twinkle, planets don't . . .
Mercury —named for the Messenger of the Gods and the God of Trade ~ is the fastest moving of all the planets.
Venus ~ namesake for the Goddess of Love and Beauty ~ is sometimes referred to as 'the brightest star in the sky' or 'the morning star', but is about the same size as the planet Earth. It is covered in clouds consisting mainly of sulphuric acid and so dense that they reflect about 75% of the light which touches them. Only about 1% of sunlight penetrates and reaches the surface of the planet.

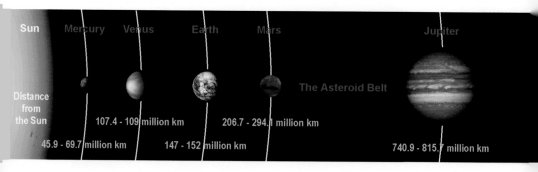

Sun	Mercury	Venus	Earth	Mars		Jupiter
					The Asteroid Belt	
Distance from the Sun	107.4 - 109 million km		206.7 - 294.1 million km			
45.9 - 69.7 million km		147 - 152 million km				740.9 - 815.7 million km

Earth ~ named for Ge or Gaia, wife of Uranus of Heaven ~ is probably the most beautiful planet in our solar system.

Mars is the name of the God of War ~ and is referred to as 'The Red Planet'. There is probably more iron ore on Mars than any other planet in the system. The rock surfaces have oxidised to give it its red colour. Mars has two tiny moons, Phobos and Deimos, like two small potatoes. It is believed that water is to be found in frozen form at Mars' polar caps.

Asteroids ~ The Asteroid Belt, lying between Mars and Jupiter, is made up of rocky material ranging in size between small dust particles to larger rocks, 6-700km and 270,000km in diameter.

Jupiter, King of the Heavens after he usurped the throne of his father, Saturn, is the name of the largest planet. It consists mainly of hydrogen gas and helium, ammonia and methane. It has 28 moons, the most obvious being the four Galilean moons: Io, Europa, Ganymede and Callisto. Jupiter *gives off twice* as much heat as it receives from the Sun.

Saturn ~ God of Time, leader of the Titans and Jupiter's father ~ is a planet made mostly of liquid hydrogen ~ which has only about 70% the density of water. Saturn would *float* in an ocean if there were one large enough. Saturn's rings are very thin, about 100 metres thick, yet they are about 270,000 km in diameter. Saturn has 30 moons, the largest of which is Titan.

Uranus, the God of Heaven, husband of Ge and father of the Titans, is a planet with 21 moons.

Neptune ~ God of the Sea ~ names this planet with 8 moons, the largest of which is Triton.

Pluto ~ God of the Underworld ~ is the last planet and has a moon called Charon.

Our Solar System

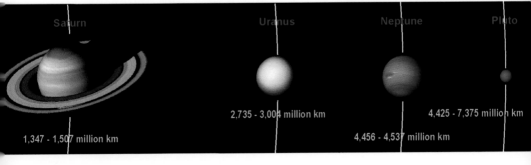

Saturn   Uranus   Neptune   Pluto

2,735 - 3,004 million km   4,425 - 7,375 million km

1,347 - 1,507 million km   4,456 - 4,537 million km

Some planets, including Earth, have satellites revolving around them. We call ours the **Moon**. The origin of the Moon remains a mystery. Nobody is really sure where and how it came into being. Some theories hold that the Moon is a part of our Earth that was blown away after a large meteorite strike, others see it as random space-junk captured by the Earth's gravitational field.

Stories from mythology attribute diverse origins and powers to the Moon. The Moon, in conjunction with the Sun, has a profound effect on nature, the tides and animal habits. For this reason the Moon was seen as one of the most powerful of the celestial bodies. Myths about the Moon often strongly reflect the culture from which the legend originated.

In hunter-gatherer societies, the Moon was usually portrayed as masculine. As these societies made the transition to an agricultural way of life, they began to see the Moon as feminine and to portray it as a nurturing body.

In the old days, people sowed their crops in the first quarter of a waxing moon and harvested them at the waning moon. They worked with the rhythm of nature. In France, towards the end of the nineteenth-century, a special timber certificate was issued if the timber had been felled when the moon was waning. This meant that there was less sap in the wood and less likelihood for the timber to warp.

Occasionally a halo is seen around the moon.

This is caused by ice particles in the Earth's upper atmosphere in which we see the light of the Moon refracted.

The halo is a sign that it will probably rain.

A story from South Australia calls the Moon, Meeka, and the Sun, Ngangaru.

Meeka and Ngangaru lived in a cave near where the moon goes down. Meeka the Moon was a clever chap. He always knew when it was going to rain. He made himself a rain-shelter ~ which is seen, from Earth, as a halo around the Moon.

The Valley of the Moons

Another Aboriginal story tells of the birth of the Full Moon, its place in the sky and why it wanes . . . The Valley of the Moons, it is told, is a very special place with the most fertile soil on Earth. The trees in this valley grow to great heights before they flower and fruit. Their fruits are baby moons which only grow and mature quite slowly. When the moons become teenagers they break away from their parent trees and float through the valley, drifting around until they are ready to take their place in the sky. This they do, one by one. The old Sun Woman shines down on the young Moons and gives them warmth while they are growing up in the Valley. But as soon as the Sun sees a Moon in *her* territory, the Sky, she suddenly turns into a jealous vampire. She races across the skies, attacking the Moon who's just taken his place. With her searing fingers, she tears him apart, piece by piece until there is nothing left but gleaming fragments ~ which she flings away. These are the stars.

The Boy-Moon Baloo

An Aboriginal story from New South Wales, Australia, has the Sun as a beautiful Maiden, Ghi, who attracts many lovers . . . One day, Ghi noticed a most handsome youth named Baloo and asked him to marry her. He pondered for a while and then said, 'Ah . . . no, thanks . . . You've had too many lovers! ' As you can imagine, the Sun's love turned to anger, her anger to hate and she conspired with powerful spirits to turn Baloo into the Moon and send him sailing through the night sky. At night you can see him trying to flee from Ghi. Moon Baloo is destined to remain in the night sky for most of each month, except for a few nights when he can escape, disguised as Gowa-gay, the Emu Bird in the sky.

The Boomerang Moon

An Aboriginal story from Cape York also relates how the Moon got into the sky . . .

The people wanted some light at night in order to be able to walk about safely, and so the children could play close to the camp. Someone suggested that they gather great piles of firewood and light a huge fire each evening. Others argued against this because after a while they might destroy the landscape if they burnt all the grass, bushes and trees. One young man suggested that a great piece of wood he had gathered be polished until it shone like the sun on a river. Then, if it were flung up into the sky, this great polished boomerang could light up the night. Men could then hunt, women could find food, children could play safely and animals too would be able to find their ways here and there. So, it was decided . . .

Many days were spent working, cutting and polishing the wood until it glistened in the early morning light. When at last it was ready, each young man came forward to try to lift the great boomerang and heave it into the sky. Each strained, grunting and groaning, but to no avail. It could not be lifted. It was too heavy.

56

An old man with spindly arms and legs came forward and asked quietly and politely, 'May I try, please?' The young men were scornful and said, 'Sit down, old man! If we cannot do it, how can you ?' Some of the older, wiser men called out 'Respect your elders! Let him try! You've failed. Let *him* try!' The old man with spindly arms and legs took hold of the boomerang and carried it to the top of a great sand dune. With trembling arms he raised the boomerang over his head and slowly but surely lifted it up into the night sky.

So today when we see a waxing moon it is once again, that great shining boomerang reminding us to respect those older, wiser, more experienced than ourselves.

The Stars

How far away are the stars?

Distance in space is measured in light years.

Light travels at a speed of approximately 300,000 kilometres *per second*.

The Moon is one quarter the size of the Earth and is about 397,000 kilometres away so reflected light takes, from the Moon, about 1 and 1/3 seconds to reach us. The light from the Sun takes about 8 minutes and 15 seconds to get here.

Alpha Centauri is 4.3 light years away.

The star **Achernar** is 85 light years away.

If you have a parent or a grandparent who is about 85 years old then the light which you see *today* as Achernar, *left* that star at about the time your grandparent was born.

The star **Canopus** is about 200 light years away so the light we see from it now, left the star at about the time Captain James Cook arrived in Australia. Many stars are hundreds, thousands and tens of thousands of light years away: so, when we are looking at the stars we are also looking *into the past* because of the length of time the light takes to reach Earth.

How old are the stars?

We can estimate the age of star by its colour.

Blue stars are young, white stars are adult, yellow stars are middle-aged, orange stars are getting pensioned off and red stars are on the way out! Our sun, a yellow star, is middle-aged or about four and a half thousand million years old.

Shooting Stars. People often feel a sense of wonder and excitement when they see a shooting star. Some cultures look on it as a sign of good fortune to spot a shooting star, and say that you should make a wish.

Some Aboriginal people see a shooting star as a bad omen, signifying that someone has died.

A shooting star is a piece of rock or a collection of space dust which comes from deep space. It enters our atmosphere at great speed, which generally results in it burning up or landing on the ground as a tektite. The burning trail is what we see.

Larger pieces of rock are commonly known as meteorites, which can cause devastation if they collide with Earth. In Siberia in 1908, there was an enormous explosion after a meteorite weighing about 40,000 tons crashed into a forest, devastating the area and creating a crater of over fifty square kilometres.

Followers of Islam who make the pilgrimage to Mecca, pay homage to the Ka'aba, 'The House of God', which is a small building that contains 'The Black Stone'. The Black Stone is reputed to have fallen to Earth from the heavens as a 'shooting star'.

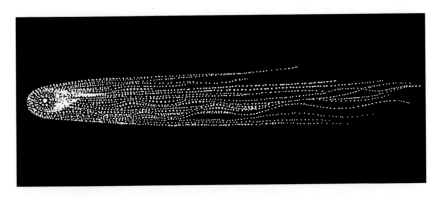

Comets have been sources of both terror and wonder for centuries, and were seen as omens of doom.

They were said to bring tidings of death for emperors in China and were associated with war, pestilence and disease in Greece.

To the ancient Persians, they were wicked fairies.

In Germany, an epidemic of sneezing sickness in cats was once blamed on a comet.

During the nineteenth century, bad weather was associated with comets. Recently, some say that the dramatic effect of the Shoemaker-Levy comet as it partially impacted on Jupiter, together with the coming of the Hyatake and Hale-Bopp comets, caused dramatic weather effects around the world.

Sightings of comets are recorded on Babylonian tablets and have been observed for centuries.

There are millions of comets in the Oort Cloud on the fringe of our solar system. These comets are mostly ice and dust. One theory suggests that gravitational attraction from a passing star, or, colliding comets, nudges these comets out towards our Sun. Heat from the Sun's radiation vaporises the frozen gas, which is fanned by solar winds to give the comets their tails. There is a group of comets known as the Kuiper Belt found just beyond Pluto.

Halley's Comet

The Universality of the Spirit of the Night Sky

The Pleiades, or *the Seven Sisters*, in the constellation Taurus the Bull, is an open cluster of about 100 stars but we only see six or seven with the naked eye.

This pretty star cluster has captured the imagination of people all over the world. The striking similarity between the stories told by different peoples about these stars presents us with a mystery scholars are attempting to solve today. Here are three of the many stories which talk of the Pleiades as 'Seven Sisters' . . .

The Pleiades

The Seven Sisters of Ancient Greece

The Greeks saw the Pleiades as the seven sisters who were the beautiful daughters of Atlas and Pleione.

They were all married to gods except the youngest sister who was married to an ordinary man. She was embarrassed by this, and tried to avoid attraction: which is why hers is the faintest of the seven visible stars.

The sisters were seen, at one point, by Orion the Hunter, who fell in love with all of them and gave chase.

Zeus felt sorry for the sisters and changed them into doves who flew away and later became stars in the sky.

From Indonesia, there is the story of Jakup-Tarup, a hunter from the forests.

Jakup-Tarup saw seven beautiful maidens come down from the night sky for a swim in a rock pool deep in the forest. It was a beautiful evening, the moon shimmering on the forest foliage, and the water softly rippling as the sisters swam. Jakup-Tarup crept closer. The radiant beauty of these lovely girls set his heart pounding.

He tried to think of how to capture one of the girls before they discovered him and flew away. He found where they had left their clothes and stole the dress of the youngest girl. He hid it in the forest.

When the sisters finished their swim, they dressed themselves and returned to the sky. While the youngest sister searched for her clothes, Jakup-Tarup appeared and offered to help her.

They never found the clothes, but the young girl stayed a while with Jakup-Tarup. She eventually gave in and agreed to marry him. She accepted him on the condition that he would never, ever look into her cooking pot. If he did, she said, she would return to the night sky.

Jakup-Tarup agreed to this request . . . It was not long before they were graced with a young son . . .

Jakup-Tarup became more and more curious, wondering why their store of rice never diminished. One day while his wife was out, he looked into her cooking pot. All he saw there was a single grain of rice. When his wife returned she knew that he had broken his word. Thereafter, they had to cook and grow rice as all other mortals did.

After her husband broke his promise, she decided to return to the night sky. She found her clothes, which he'd hidden in their hut. Before leaving, she told her Jakup-Tarup that, because they had a young child, she would return every now and then. The Moon would appear and be her breast with which she would feed the child.

An African story describes seven sisters who descended from the skies.

These maidens were radiantly beautiful and came from the sky to swim in a waterhole. After removing their robes they were spied by a wandering herdsman who crept up for a closer look.

Upon seeing their exquisite beauty he began to lust after them. He particularly desired the youngest because she was the most beautiful.

When they were not looking the herdsman took the robes of the youngest sister and hid them. When the girls finished bathing, six of the sisters were able to return to the sky, but the seventh had to look for her clothes.

The herdsman revealed himself and offered to help the distraught maiden. Unable to find her robes, the sister agreed to stay with the herdsman and, after a while, they were married. She agreed to stay with him on the condition that he would never look into a pot she had with her.

One day however, while she was out, the temptation was too great for the herdsman and he looked into the pot. And what do you think he saw? Nothing!

When his wife returned, woman's intuition being what it is, she knew he had broken his word. She told him that she would now be returning to the night sky. She looked around the hut, discovered her missing robes and left.

This story has been interpreted as meaning that when the herdsman looked into the pot, he was actually looking into himself. By breaking his promise, he had lost his soul, his being had become empty ~ and no good woman could stay with a man who had lost his inner content.

Why is this star cluster so fascinating for so many peoples and cultures? How is it that the stories about them are so similar?

Part of the magic of the night skies is that they hold many secrets and mysteries, whose answers may lead us closer to the realities of life.

The Galaxy

Our solar system sits within our galaxy, the Milky Way.

A galaxy is like an enormous cluster or gigantic family of millions of stars that move together with each other. The stars we see are immense balls of gas burning much like our Sun.

Some stars are thousands of times larger than our Sun. Others are much smaller. So we can correctly think of stars as being individual suns that are so far away we only see them as small points of light.

Our galaxy is spiral-shaped and our solar system is a very, very, very small part of it, situated near the end of one of its spiral arms. From Earth, we can see other galaxies as faint clouds in the night sky. In our local group of galaxies there are about thirty. With our naked eye we can see the Large and Small Magellanic Clouds in the Southern Hemisphere, but they cannot be seen in the Northern Hemisphere. The Andromeda Galaxy, also part of our local group, can be seen with our naked eye in both the Northern and Southern Hemisphere, and is 2.2 million light years away.

In the Greek mythology, Queen Andromeda was chained by Medusa to rocks near the sea. Medusa put her there as an offering to the mighty sea monster, Kraken. Fortunately, Andromeda was saved by Perseus.

Sombrero Galaxy

Stars are grouped together in different ways within galaxies: Binary stars, for example, appear as single stars to the naked eye, but are actually doubles or more than one. Alpha Centauri, which we recognise as one of the pointers to the Southern Cross, is in fact three stars, but other binaries may have more stars.

Clusters of stars appear as small fuzzy patches of light in the sky. Some may contain up to one million stars, such as **Omega Centauri**, a globular cluster 17,000 light years away.

Omega Centauri

The Universe

Our galaxy is as a speck of dust in the Sahara when compared with everything else that is out there in the Universe. The Milky Way is part of its 'local' cluster of 30 galaxies, which in turn, is part of a Super Cluster of between 300 and 400 galaxies. There are, literally, millions of galaxies within the known universe.

As knowledge advances, so does our understanding of the Universe. Hundreds of years ago, the world was thought to be flat, but today it is understood to be round.

The meaning of the word 'universe' is 'all knowable things': so, as knowledge advances, so does the boundary of the Universe. As if this alone is not difficult enough to comprehend, the latest theories suggest that there are other universes beyond our own.

It is difficult for us to visualise something on such a huge scale, let alone understand it.

A story which may help put this into perspective comes from Indonesia. A Dayak man from Kalimantan describes how, in spiritual meditation, he left his body and moved into the sky and beyond. When he looked back, he saw the Earth as a small cell. Travelling further he looked back at our solar system and saw it as the organ of a living being. Then, going just beyond the Milky Way, he looked back, and saw it as a fish swimming in the sea.

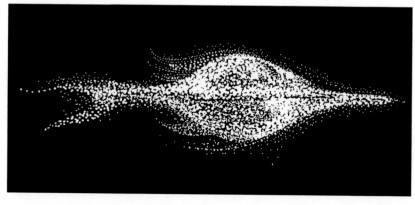

The Mystery and Meaning of It All

The night sky is one of the few things in life which is free and open to all people on earth. The wonderment and mystery of the stars and planets touch us, opening up our feelings, enabling us to look at life anew.

Scientific facts and figures are often found at the core of ancient legends and stories about the heavens.

Stories from 'the beginning of time' bring the night skies to life and help people from all over the world to connect their lives, past and present, with the movements and harmonics of the universe.

Under the night sky, we ponder the seeming insignificance of our place in the vastness of the Universe, on our origins.

We may wonder why there are so many similarities between night sky stories passed down orally from generation to generation by indigenous peoples throughout the world. The similarities suggest common origins of the tales, and, of us all. Telling them brings us closer to one another and creates bridges between peoples and cultures.

These stories which have survived for generations are remembered and recorded today because they *still* serve a purpose: they can help guide us on our journey into the new millennium.

Indigenous peoples have always kept knowledge which modern science is only now able to verify with the aid of powerful telescopes and sophisticated technologies.

How did the African Dogon people know, as long as five thousand years ago, that Sirius has a little white dwarf star that takes fifty years to go in an elliptical orbit around the larger star?

Our astronomers only found out about 135 years ago! Could it also be true that the Sirius Star System contains the origins of our own human civilisation on Earth?

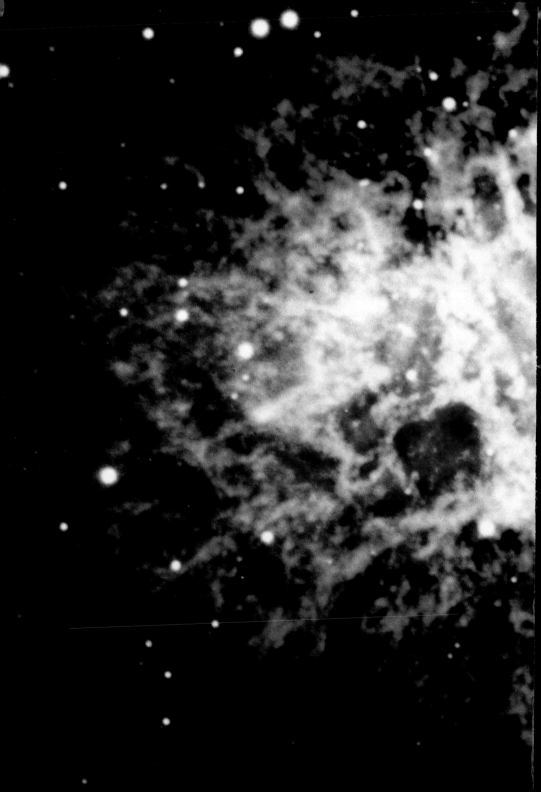

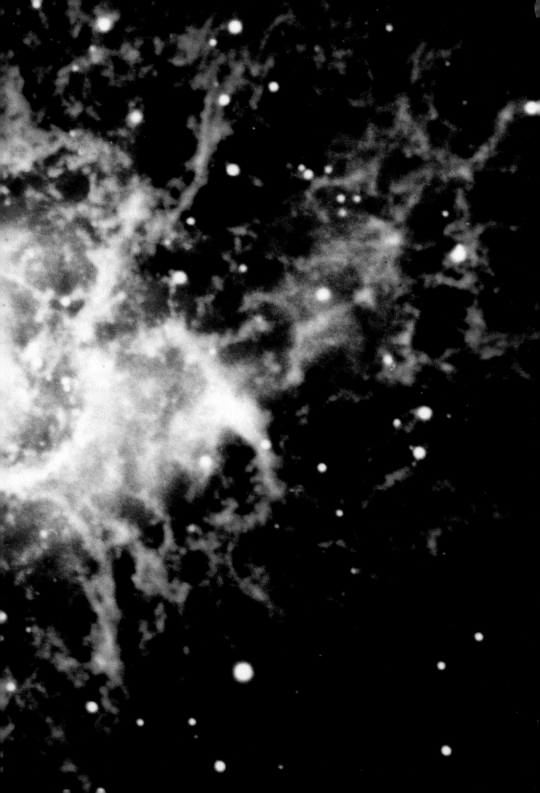

In his book, 'The Sirius Mystery', Robert K.G. Temple says that the Dogon claim that it does.

Robert Bauval and Adrian Gilbert in 'The Orion Mystery' suggest that the Giza pyramids in Egypt are sited in alignment with Orion's Belt, and that the pyramids are more likely to date from 10,450 B.C. than 2,500 B.C..

Graham Hancock in 'Fingerprints of the Gods' suggests that the pyramids have a message for us today in the new millenium.

Ancient stories, common to many countries, often include star themes ~ as well as themes like Oedipus, and The Great Flood.

One such story from Indonesia describes a place called Batu Banama, Boat-Rock, in Central Kalimantan where there is a large boulder jutting out of the jungle ground.

The Dayaks say there was a time when Central Kalimantan was under the sea, many thousands of years ago. At that time a young woman had a small boy who was naughty ~ so naughty that she hit him on the head with a wooden spoon, scarring his head for life. Later, he was sent far away to China to be educated and there he became a successful man of trade and business.

Wanting to return home, he procured a boat and, as he was coming into harbour, he saw a beautiful woman.

He fell in love with her and they were married.

One day, when she held his head in her lap, she saw his scar and, when she asked him how he got it, he said that his mother had hit him on the head when he was a small boy. She realised then that she was his mother.

The next time he put to sea, angry that he had married his mother, God sank the boat.

So here is another universal story ~ with the Oedipus theme.

The inner meaning of the story, it is said, is not that a man married his mother in the literal sense; but that a man who gets caught up in materialism and loses his spiritual connections can make great mistakes.

The story goes on to tell that there was a time when human beings were on Earth before this Age ~ a time Man was more advanced than today ~ able to travel to the outer limits of our galaxy.

But the people then lost their way and became greedy and arrogant. They saw themselves as gods and forgot God.

The Earth started to move towards the Sun and, even with all their technology, they were powerless to stop it.

Suddenly, the Earth stopped of its own accord and tilted on its axis. Great flooding occurred and most of the people perished. Those who survived the shock had the memory erased from their hearts and minds and the only way they could access knowledge of it was through their spiritual or intuitive nature . . .

In June 1996, a 'Star Knowledge Conference and Sun Dance' was held on a Sioux reservation in North Dakota. Indigenous elders and leaders from Hopi, Sioux, Yaqui, Mayan, Maori and Lapland peoples announced that the time had come for them to share some of their traditional knowledge about our common origins. These indigenous elders claim that they have ancient and continuing communication with people from the Stars. Old stories, previously guarded secretly, could now be made public . . .

As we study the past and unlock some of its secrets through archaeological discovery, scientific research, intuition, spiritual awareness and other means, we find keys to Present and Future. Increasing awareness and understanding of our place in the vast scheme of being and things can help us reconcile the Past with the Present and to find harmony and hope for the Future.

Acknowledgements

This book was written at Ayers Rock Resort, Central Australia, and it could not have been written without the help of my friends and fellow star talkers who all added personal touches from their star presentations at the "Sound of Silence" desert dinner: Peter Medley, Erica Mors, Arifah Burra, Samantha Essex, Hussein Burra, Lorna Adlem. Special thanks to Peter, Erica and Arifah who all collaborated with the writing; to Michael Maher who introduced me to the night skies; and Peter Franklind for his technical help.

I would like to thank Akira Fuji, well known astronomer and photographer, for his generosity in allowing me to use his photographs of the night sky; the Anglo Australian Observatory and Hussein Burra for the use of their photographs; Rahman Connelly and Bradford Temple who donated seed money to the project; Luqman McKingley and his associates at Starlight Press for the drawings, illustrations, design and layout work which they contributed ~ and for bringing the book to press.

Ayers Rock Resort Management provide the "Sound of Silence" dinner in the desert and they have supported this book to publication. Many thanks to all their management team and to all the catering staff who do so much to make each night a memorable night.

Bibliography

Allen, Richard Hinkley, *Star Names, Their Lore and Meaning*, Dover Publications, USA, 1963.

Bauval, Robert & **Handcock**, Graham, *The Message of the Sphinx*, Three Rivers Press, 1996.

Bauval, Robert & **Gilbert**, Adrian, *The Orion Mystery*, Crown Trade Paperbacks, New York, 1994.

Burnham, Robert, Jr, *Burnham's Celestial Handbook: An Observer's Guide to the Universe Beyond the Solar System*, Vol. 1, 2, 3, Dover Publications, Ed. 1978.

Cornelius, Geoffrey, *The Starlore Handbook*, Duncan Baird Publishers, 1997.

Cornelius, Geoffrey & **Devereux**, Paul, *The Secret Language of the Stars and Planets*, Universal International Australia, 1997.

D'Arcy, Peter Ed & **Sutton**, Margo, *The Emu in the Sky*, National Science & Technology Centre, Canberra, 1993/4.

Ellyard, David & **Tirion**, Wil, *The Southern Sky Guide*, Cambridge University Press, 1993.

Hancock, Graham, *Fingerprints of the Gods*, Crown Publishers, New York, 1995.

Hulley, Charles & **Roberts**, Ainslie, *Dreamtime Moon*, Reed Books, 1996.

Mountford, Charles & **Roberts**, Ainslie, *The Dreamtime Series*, Art Australia, 1989.

Plant, Malcolm, *Dictionary of Space*, Longman, 1986.

Ridpath, Ian & **Tirion**, Wil, *Stars and Planets*, Collins Pocket Guide, 2nd ed., New York, 1994.

Roberts & Roberts, *Echoes of the Dreamtime*, J. M. Dent Pty. Ltd., Melbourne, 1988.

Sullivan, William, *The Secret of the Incas*, Three Rivers Press, New York.

Temple, Robert, K. G., *The Sirius Mystery*, St. Matin's Press, New York, 1976.

Verdet, Jean-Pierre, *The Sky Mystery, Magic and Myth, Discoveries*, Harry N. Abrams, Inc., 1992.

Willis, Roy, **Ed.**, *World Mythology*, RD Press, Australia.

Sky & Telescope Magazine, Sept., 1997.